Skills Builders

Fractions, Decimals and Percentages

YEAR 4

Joanne Howes, Richard Cooper and Andrew Thrower

RISING ★ STARS

Rising Stars UK Ltd, 7 Hatchers Mews, Bermondsey Street, London SE1 3GS
www.risingstars-uk.com

Every effort has been made to trace copyright holders and obtain their permission for the use of copyright materials. The publishers will gladly receive information enabling them to rectify any error or omission in subsequent editions.

All facts are correct at time of going to press.

Published 2013
Text, design and layout © 2013 Rising Stars UK Ltd

Project manager: Dawn Booth
Editorial: David Hemsley
Proofreader: Bobby Francis
Design: Words & Pictures, London
Cover design: Amina Dudhia
Character illustration: Louisa Burville-Riley

British Library Cataloguing-in-Publication Data
A CIP record for this book is available from the British Library.

ISBN 978-0-85769-690-8
Printed in Singapore by Craft Print International Limited

MIX
Paper from responsible sources
FSC
www.fsc.org   FSC® C023802

Skills Builders: Fractions, Decimals and Percentages

YEAR
4

Contents

How to use this book

The *Skills Builders Fractions, Decimals and Percentages* series is designed to help you get to grips with this tricky topic.

The key thing to remember about fractions, decimals and percentages is:

> They are all different ways of expressing the same amount.

For example, 25% is the same as $\frac{1}{4}$ which is also the same as 0.25.

1 The introduction to each spread gives you an idea of the sort of problems you are likely to see and helps you to understand what maths you need to use.

2 The flow chart takes you through an example problem step-by-step. This is important when you are answering questions about fractions, decimals and percentages.

3 Hints and tips section gives you useful ideas for completing the problems on the following page. These are the things you need to remember if you are doing a quiz or test!

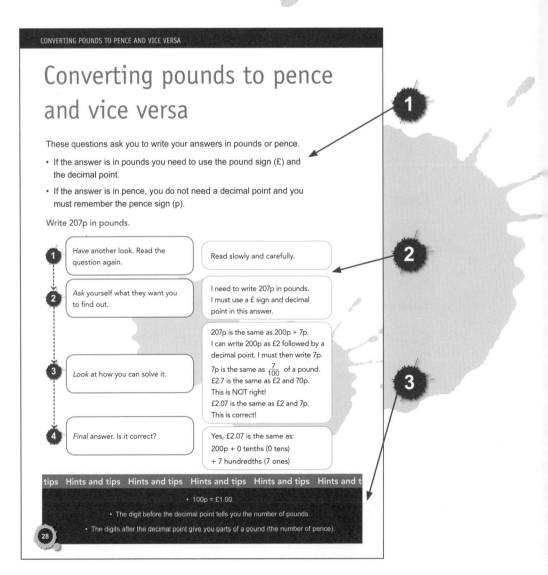

The questions get harder as you go down the page.

4 Section 1 questions are fairly straightforward and help you to practise your skills.

5 Section 2 questions are a bit harder but will help you to remember all the key points.

6 The Challenge sections are really tough and sometimes mean that you can make up games and your own questions! They can be great fun!

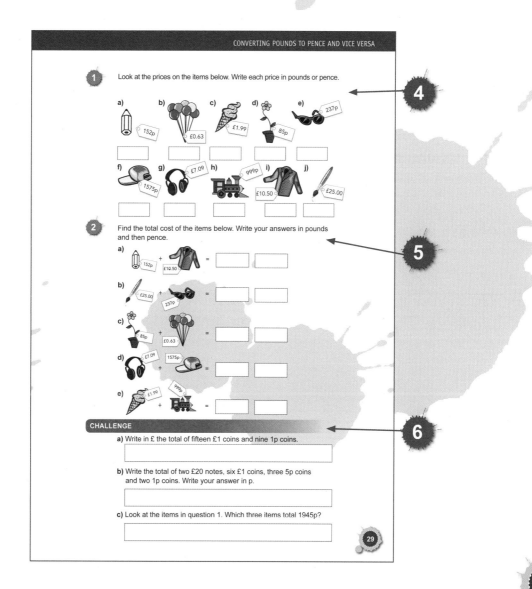

CONVERTING POUNDS TO PENCE AND VICE VERSA

1 Look at the prices on the items below. Write each price in pounds or pence.

a) 152p b) £0.63 c) £1.99 d) 85p e) 237p

f) 1575p g) £7.09 h) 999p i) £10.50 j) £25.00

2 Find the total cost of the items below. Write your answers in pounds and then pence.

a) 152p + £10.50 =

b) £25.00 + 237p =

c) 85p + £0.63 =

d) £7.09 + 1575p =

e) £1.99 + 999p =

CHALLENGE

a) Write in £ the total of fifteen £1 coins and nine 1p coins.

b) Write the total of two £20 notes, six £1 coins, three 5p coins and two 1p coins. Write your answer in p.

c) Look at the items in question 1. Which three items total 1945p?

29

5

Ten top tips

1 Work through each question step-by-step. Follow the flow chart.

Every time you approach a fractions question, remember these four steps:

Have another look. Read the question again.

Ask yourself what they want you to find out.

Look at how you can solve it.

Final answer. Is it correct?

We can remember this by looking at the first letter of each step.

They read HALF!

2 Always *show your working or "method"*. This will help you to keep track of what you have done and may help you to get extra marks.

3 Always *include your units* in the answer. If you don't, you won't get full marks.

4 When you first read through a question, *underline important words and numbers*. This will help you to remember the important bits!

5 *Draw a picture* to help you. Sometimes a question is easier if you can "see" it.

Drawing 6 apples can help you if you need to divide them!

6 If the problem has a number of steps, break it down and *do one step at a time.*

7 When *checking your answers*, look at the inverse operation.

8 Sometimes an answer will "sound right". Read it out (quietly) and listen. *Does it make sense?*

9 If you are using measurements (grams, litres, cm), make sure that the *units are the same* before you calculate.

10 Once again! *Remember the mnemonic HALF!*

Recognising fractions

Some questions ask you to find a fraction of a shape.

It is important that the shape is divided into *equal* parts.

What fraction of the circle is shaded?

1 *Have* another look. Read the question again.

Read slowly and carefully. Look at the fraction.

2 *Ask* yourself what they want you to find out.

I need to know how many parts are shaded and write it as a fraction.

3 *Look* at how you can solve it.

I have to count how many parts there are altogether and then count how many of them are shaded. There are 8 parts altogether and 3 of them are shaded.

4 *Final* answer. Is it correct?

3 parts out of the eight are shaded, so the answer must be $\frac{3}{8}$.

• Your answer must be written as a fraction.

The fraction shown here is $2\frac{3}{8}$.

What fraction of each shape is shaded?

a)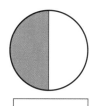

b)

c)

d)

e)

f)

2 This is the whole shape.   How much is shaded?

a)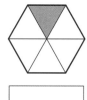

b)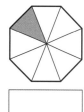

c)

d)

e)

CHALLENGE

How many shapes in each set are shaded?

a)

b)

Creating fractions

Sometimes you need to create a fraction of a shape. The top number of the fraction (the numerator) tells you how much to shade and the bottom number (the denominator) tells you how many parts there are.

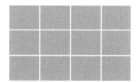

Shade $\frac{5}{12}$ of this shape.

1 *Have* another look. Read the question again.

Read slowly and carefully. Look at the fraction.

2 *Ask* yourself what they want you to find out.

I need to colour $\frac{5}{12}$. That means 5 out of the 12 parts.

3 *Look* at how you can solve it.

I need to colour in 5 parts of the shape.

4 *Final* answer. Is it correct?

Yes, I have shaded 5 of the 12 parts, which is $\frac{5}{12}$.

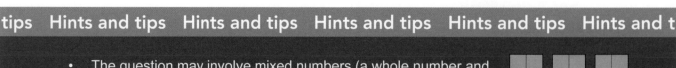

tips   **Hints and tips**   **Hints and tips**   **Hints and tips**   **Hints and tips**   **Hints and t**

- The question may involve mixed numbers (a whole number and a fraction), e.g. $5\frac{3}{4}$. You need to shade 5 whole squares and $\frac{3}{4}$ of the other square.

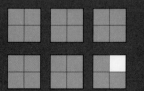

1 Colour in the fraction given for each shape.

a)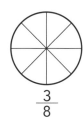

$\frac{3}{8}$

b)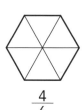

$\frac{4}{6}$

c)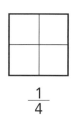

$\frac{1}{4}$

d)

$\frac{6}{9}$

e)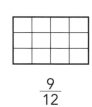

$\frac{9}{12}$

f)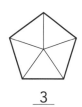

$\frac{3}{5}$

2 For these shapes, colour in the mixed number.

a) $5\frac{3}{8}$

b) $3\frac{2}{6}$

c) $1\frac{8}{9}$

d) $2\frac{2}{4}$

e) $4\frac{10}{12}$

CHALLENGE

You need squared paper.

a) Draw squares divided into quarters. How many different ways can you colour in half?

b) Draw rectangles divided into sixths. How many different ways can you colour in half?

c) Draw some rectangles. How many different ways can you divide them into eighths?

Equivalent fractions

Equivalent fractions are fractions that are the same size as each other.

You will need to know the equivalence between:

- halves, quarters and eighths

- tenths and fifths

- thirds and sixths

How many sixths make one half?

1 *Have* another look. Read the question again.

Read slowly and carefully. Look at the words "sixth" and "half".

2 *Ask* yourself what they want you to find out.

A sixth is 1 part of a whole divided into 6 equal parts. A half is 1 part of a whole divided into 2 equal parts. I need to know how many sixths are the same as 1 half.

3 *Look* at how you can solve it.

I could draw a rectangle and divide it into six equal parts. If I colour half of the rectangle, I have coloured 3 parts ($\frac{3}{6}$).

4 *Final* answer. Is it correct?

3 sixths make 1 half. I can check by dividing 6 by 2. $6 \div 2 = 3$

- Drawing pictures or a fraction wall can help you find equivalent fractions.

1			
$\frac{1}{2}$		$\frac{1}{2}$	
$\frac{1}{3}$	$\frac{1}{3}$	$\frac{1}{3}$	
$\frac{1}{4}$	$\frac{1}{4}$	$\frac{1}{4}$	$\frac{1}{4}$

1 Write these equivalent fractions.

a)

b)

c)

d)

e)

f)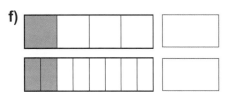

2 Write one equivalent fraction for each of the following.

a) $\dfrac{4}{16}$

b) $\dfrac{3}{6}$

c) $\dfrac{6}{8}$

d) $\dfrac{8}{10}$

e) $\dfrac{3}{12}$

f) $\dfrac{2}{10}$

CHALLENGE

Continue the pattern with three more equivalent fractions.

a) $\dfrac{1}{3}$ $\dfrac{2}{6}$ $\dfrac{3}{9}$

b) $\dfrac{1}{2}$ $\dfrac{2}{4}$ $\dfrac{3}{6}$

c) $\dfrac{1}{4}$ $\dfrac{2}{8}$ $\dfrac{3}{12}$

d) $\dfrac{1}{5}$ $\dfrac{2}{10}$ $\dfrac{3}{15}$

Fractions of numbers

Finding a fraction of a number is the same as division. For example, finding $\frac{1}{2}$ of a number is the same as dividing the number by 2. Finding a quarter of a number is the same as dividing by 4.

What is $\frac{1}{3}$ of 12?

1 *Have* another look. Read the question again.

Look at the fraction and the number.

2 *Ask* yourself what they want you to find out.

The bottom number in the fraction tells me what I need to divide by. $\frac{1}{3}$ of 12 is the same as dividing 12 by 3. So $12 \div 3 = ?$

3 *Look* at how you can solve it.

I could use 12 counters and divide them into 3 groups. How many counters does each group have? Each group has 4.

4 *Final* answer. Is it correct?

$12 \div 3 = 4$, so $\frac{1}{3}$ of 12 is 4.
Let's check by multiplication:
$3 \times ? = 12 \quad 3 \times 4 = 12$
Yes, 4 is correct.

tips   Hints and tips   Hints and tips   Hints and tips   Hints and tips   Hints and t

- Learning your multiplication tables will help with finding fractions of numbers.

- Use counters or cubes to help with dividing.

1 Join the fractions to the correct answers.

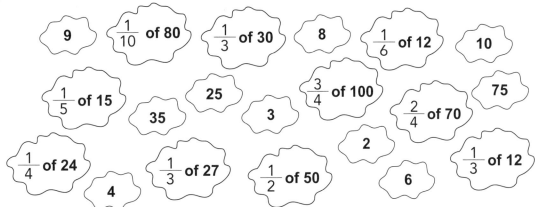

9    $\frac{1}{10}$ of 80 $\frac{1}{3}$ of 30   8 $\frac{1}{6}$ of 12   10

$\frac{1}{5}$ of 15   25 $\frac{3}{4}$ of 100   75

35   3 $\frac{2}{4}$ of 70

$\frac{1}{4}$ of 24 $\frac{1}{3}$ of 27 $\frac{1}{2}$ of 50   2 $\frac{1}{3}$ of 12

4   6

2 Draw pictures on a separate piece of paper to help you work out these fractions.

a) What fraction of 36 is 9?

b) What fraction of 54 is 6?

c) What fraction of 64 is 8?

d) What fraction of 132 is 11?

e) What fraction of 100 is 10?

CHALLENGE

What fraction of the larger object is the smaller object?

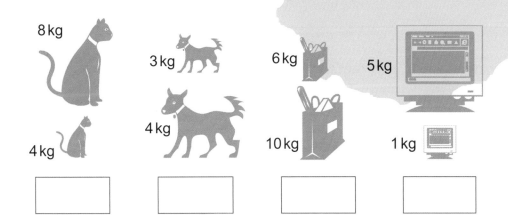

8 kg

3 kg

6 kg

5 kg

4 kg

4 kg

10 kg

1 kg

Ordering fractions

When ordering fractions, you need to look at both the top number (the numerator) and the bottom number (the denominator).

Put the following fractions in order, starting with the smallest:

$$\frac{1}{3} \quad \frac{2}{3} \quad \frac{5}{6} \quad \frac{3}{6}$$

1 *Have* another look. Read the question again.

Look at the list of fractions. Two are in thirds and two are in sixths.

2 *Ask* yourself what they want you to find out.

I need to put the fractions in order, starting with the smallest.

3 *Look* at how you can solve it.

First I need to make all the denominators the same.

I know that $\frac{1}{3}$ is the same as $\frac{2}{6}$ and $\frac{2}{3}$ is the same as $\frac{4}{6}$.

Now I can write the list in order:
$$\frac{2}{6} \quad \frac{3}{6} \quad \frac{4}{6} \quad \frac{5}{6}$$

4 *Final* answer. Is it correct?

I must remember to convert the $\frac{2}{6}$ back to $\frac{1}{3}$ and the $\frac{4}{6}$ back to $\frac{2}{3}$.

The answer is: $\frac{1}{3} \quad \frac{3}{6} \quad \frac{2}{3} \quad \frac{5}{6}$

tips Hints and tips Hints and tips Hints and tips Hints and tips Hints and t

- Use your knowledge of equivalent fractions to help you.

- If you convert fractions to help you order them, remember to convert them back at the end.

1 Write these fractions in order of size, starting with the smallest.

a) $\dfrac{2}{4}$ $\dfrac{3}{4}$ $\dfrac{4}{4}$ $\dfrac{1}{4}$ [ ]

b) $\dfrac{2}{10}$ $\dfrac{5}{10}$ $\dfrac{10}{10}$ $\dfrac{7}{10}$ [ ]

c) $\dfrac{5}{5}$ $\dfrac{1}{5}$ $\dfrac{4}{5}$ $\dfrac{2}{5}$ [ ]

d) $\dfrac{1}{7}$ $\dfrac{4}{7}$ $\dfrac{3}{7}$ $\dfrac{6}{7}$ [ ]

e) $\dfrac{3}{8}$ $\dfrac{1}{8}$ $\dfrac{6}{8}$ $\dfrac{8}{8}$ [ ]

f) $\dfrac{8}{12}$ $\dfrac{4}{12}$ $\dfrac{10}{12}$ $\dfrac{6}{12}$ [ ]

g) $\dfrac{5}{6}$ $\dfrac{2}{6}$ $\dfrac{1}{6}$ $\dfrac{3}{6}$ [ ]

h) $\dfrac{9}{9}$ $\dfrac{5}{9}$ $\dfrac{7}{9}$ $\dfrac{2}{9}$ [ ]

2 Write these fractions in order of size, starting with the smallest.

a) $\dfrac{2}{4}$ $\dfrac{3}{8}$ $\dfrac{6}{8}$ $\dfrac{1}{4}$ [ ]

b) $\dfrac{1}{2}$ $\dfrac{6}{6}$ $\dfrac{2}{6}$ $\dfrac{1}{6}$ [ ]

c) $\dfrac{1}{6}$ $\dfrac{1}{3}$ $\dfrac{3}{6}$ $\dfrac{2}{3}$ [ ]

d) $\dfrac{1}{3}$ $\dfrac{2}{6}$ $\dfrac{3}{3}$ $\dfrac{1}{2}$ [ ]

e) $\dfrac{9}{10}$ $\dfrac{8}{10}$ $\dfrac{3}{5}$ $\dfrac{1}{5}$ [ ]

f) $\dfrac{3}{4}$ $\dfrac{1}{4}$ $\dfrac{3}{8}$ $\dfrac{7}{8}$ [ ]

CHALLENGE

a) Which of these fractions are greater than one half? Which are less than one half? Write each fraction in the correct box.

$\dfrac{5}{6}$ $\quad$ $\dfrac{1}{6}$ $\quad$ $\dfrac{3}{3}$ $\quad$ $\dfrac{2}{3}$ $\quad$ $\dfrac{2}{10}$ $\quad$ $\dfrac{8}{12}$ $\quad$ $\dfrac{4}{5}$ $\quad$ $\dfrac{2}{5}$ $\quad$ $\dfrac{3}{4}$ $\quad$ $\dfrac{3}{8}$

More than $\dfrac{1}{2}$ $\qquad\qquad$ Less than $\dfrac{1}{2}$

[ ] $\qquad\qquad$ [ ]

b) Write < (smaller than) or > (greater than) between each pair of fractions.

$\dfrac{1}{2}$ [ ] $\dfrac{1}{10}$

$\dfrac{1}{8}$ [ ] $\dfrac{1}{3}$

$\dfrac{1}{4}$ [ ] $\dfrac{1}{8}$

Fractions with a total of 1

Fractions are smaller parts of a whole number.

You can add two fractions together to make one whole.

Fill in the missing number in this sum: $\frac{2}{5} + ? = 1$

1 Have another look. Read the question again.

Look at the fraction.

2 Ask yourself what they want you to find out.

I need to find out what other fraction needs to be added to $\frac{2}{5}$ in order to make one whole.

3 Look at how you can solve it.

I could draw a circle divided into 5 equal parts and shade 2 of them ($\frac{2}{5}$).

How many more parts need to be shaded to complete the circle?

4 Final answer. Is it correct?

I need to shade 3 out of the 5 parts, so $\frac{3}{5}$ is the answer.

$\frac{2}{5} + \frac{3}{5} = \frac{5}{5}$ or 1

tips   Hints and tips   Hints and tips   Hints and tips   Hints and tips   Hints and t

- Look at the bottom number in the fraction (the denominator).

To make 1 the two top numbers (numerators) must add up to the same number as the denominator. The denominator stays the same. $\frac{7}{12} + ? = 1$

You need to add 5 to 7 to make 12, so $\frac{7}{12} + \frac{5}{12} = \frac{12}{12}$ or 1

1 Look at the shapes below. The fraction shows how much of the shape is shaded. Write the fraction needed to shade the whole shape.

a)

$\dfrac{2}{6}$ +

b)

$\dfrac{10}{12}$ +

c)

$\dfrac{1}{5}$ +

d)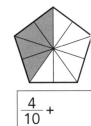

$\dfrac{4}{10}$ +

e)

$\dfrac{1}{3}$ +

f)

$\dfrac{8}{16}$ +

 2 Write another fraction next to the one given so that they total one whole.

a) $\dfrac{2}{5}$ + [ ] = 1

b) $\dfrac{2}{3}$ + [ ] = 1

c) $\dfrac{1}{4}$ + [ ] = 1

d) $\dfrac{16}{20}$ + [ ] = 1

e) $\dfrac{8}{10}$ + [ ] = 1

CHALLENGE

a) Write out more pairs of fractions that give a total of 1.

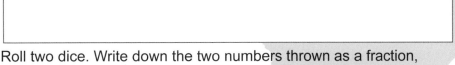

b) Roll two dice. Write down the two numbers thrown as a fraction, placing the lower number at the top. Write down the fraction you would need to make the total 1. (If you throw two numbers the same, you have already thrown 1!)

For example, if you throw a 4 and a 3, write down $\dfrac{3}{4}$. The fraction needed to make 1 is $\dfrac{1}{4}$.

Adding fractions with a common denominator

Some problems will ask you to add fractions together that have different denominators. We need to find a common denominator.

What is the total of $\frac{1}{3}$ and $\frac{3}{6}$?

1 *Have* another look. Read the question again.

What is the total of one third and three sixths?

2 *Ask* yourself what they want you to find out.

I know that $\frac{1}{3}$ is equivalent to $\frac{2}{6}$.

3 *Look* at how you can solve it.

$$\frac{1}{3} + \frac{3}{6} =$$

$$\frac{2}{6} + \frac{3}{6} = \frac{5}{6}$$

The answer is "five sixths".

4 *Final* answer. Is it correct?

Yes. I have checked my answer twice and it looks correct.

- Look at the denominators. Use your knowledge of multiplication to help you.
- Make sure that whatever you do to the denominator, you do to the numerator.

1 Add these fractions:

a) $\frac{1}{2} + \frac{1}{4} =$ ☐   b) $\frac{2}{4} + \frac{3}{8} =$ ☐

c) $\frac{1}{3} + \frac{4}{6} =$ ☐   d) $\frac{2}{5} + \frac{2}{10} =$ ☐

e) $\frac{2}{3} + \frac{1}{6} =$ ☐   f) $\frac{1}{4} + \frac{5}{8} =$ ☐

2 Colour the segments of the shapes to help you work out these fraction additions.

a) $\frac{2}{6} + \frac{1}{3} =$ ☐

b) $\frac{3}{8} + \frac{1}{4} =$ ☐

c) $\frac{1}{3} + \frac{3}{6} =$ ☐

d) $\frac{4}{8} + \dfrac{\boxed{}}{4} = \frac{3}{4}$

CHALLENGE

Can you add the following?

a) $\frac{1}{3} + \frac{4}{9} =$ ☐

b) $\frac{1}{2} + \frac{4}{8} =$ ☐

c) $\frac{1}{4} + \frac{3}{12} =$ ☐

d) $\frac{1}{3} + \frac{1}{4} =$ ☐

Subtracting fractions with a common denominator

Some problems will ask you to take one fraction away from another with different denominators.

We need to find a common denominator.

What is $\frac{2}{4} - \frac{3}{8}$?

1 *Have* another look. Read the question again.

What is three eighths subtracted from two quarters?

2 *Ask* yourself what they want you to find out.

I need to check what the fractions are and change them to a common denominator.

3 *Look* at how you can solve it.

$\frac{2}{4}$ is equivalent to $\frac{4}{8}$

$\frac{4}{8} - \frac{3}{8} = \frac{1}{8}$

So $\frac{2}{4} - \frac{3}{8} = \frac{1}{8}$

4 *Final* answer. Is it correct?

Yes. I have checked my answer twice and it looks correct.

tips **Hints and tips** **Hints and tips** **Hints and tips** **Hints and tips** **Hints and t**

- Think about which fraction is smaller.
- Does my answer make sense? (Is it too big or too small?)

Answers

Skills Builders

Fractions, Decimals and Percentages

YEAR
4

Joanne Howes,
Richard Cooper
and
Andrew Thrower

Recognising fractions (page 9)

1 a) $\frac{1}{2}$

b) $\frac{1}{4}$

c) $\frac{1}{5}$

d) $\frac{1}{6}$

e) $\frac{1}{7}$

f) $\frac{1}{8}$

2 a) $\frac{1}{2}$

b) $\frac{2}{6}$ or $\frac{1}{3}$

c) $\frac{6}{9}$ or $\frac{2}{3}$

d) $\frac{4}{5}$

e) $\frac{1}{7}$

Challenge

a) $2\frac{4}{10}$ or $2\frac{2}{5}$

b) $3\frac{1}{6}$

Creating fractions (page 11)

1 Check children's colouring.
2 Check children's colouring.
3 Check children's drawing.

Equivalent fractions (page 13)

1 a) $\frac{2}{3} = \frac{4}{6}$

b) $\frac{1}{3} = \frac{4}{12}$

c) $\frac{3}{4} = \frac{6}{8}$

d) $\frac{3}{5} = \frac{6}{10}$

e) $\frac{1}{2} = \frac{5}{10}$

f) $\frac{1}{4} = \frac{2}{8}$

2 Examples:

a) $\frac{1}{4}, \frac{2}{8}, \frac{8}{32}$

b) $\frac{1}{2}, \frac{2}{4}, \frac{5}{10}$

c) $\frac{3}{4}, \frac{9}{12}, \frac{12}{16}$

d) $\frac{4}{5}, \frac{16}{20}, \frac{24}{30}$

e) $\frac{1}{4}, \frac{4}{16}, \frac{6}{24}$

f) $\frac{1}{5}, \frac{3}{15}$

Challenge

a) $\frac{4}{12}, \frac{5}{15}, \frac{6}{18}$

b) $\frac{4}{8}, \frac{5}{10}, \frac{6}{12}$

c) $\frac{4}{16}, \frac{5}{20}, \frac{6}{24}$

d) $\frac{4}{20}, \frac{5}{25}, \frac{6}{30}$

Fractions of numbers (page 15)

1 $8 = \frac{1}{10}$ of 80; $9 = \frac{1}{3}$ of 27;

$2 = \frac{1}{6}$ of 12; $3 = \frac{1}{5}$ of 15;

$4 = \frac{1}{3}$ of 12; $6 = \frac{1}{4}$ of 24;

$10 = \frac{1}{3}$ of 30; $25 = \frac{1}{2}$ of 50;

$35 = \frac{1}{2}$ of 70; $75 = \frac{3}{4}$ of 100

2 a) $\frac{1}{4}$

b) $\frac{1}{9}$

c) $\frac{1}{8}$

d) $\frac{1}{12}$

e) $\frac{1}{10}$

Challenge

a) $\frac{1}{2}$

b) $\frac{3}{4}$

c) $\frac{3}{5}$

d) $\frac{1}{5}$

Ordering fractions (page 17)

1 a) $\frac{1}{4}, \frac{2}{4}, \frac{3}{4}, \frac{4}{4}$

b) $\frac{2}{10}, \frac{5}{10}, \frac{7}{10}, \frac{10}{10}$

c) $\frac{1}{5}, \frac{2}{5}, \frac{4}{5}, \frac{5}{5}$

d) $\frac{1}{7}, \frac{3}{7}, \frac{4}{7}, \frac{6}{7}$

e) $\frac{1}{8}, \frac{3}{8}, \frac{6}{8}, \frac{8}{8}$

f) $\frac{4}{12}, \frac{6}{12}, \frac{8}{12}, \frac{10}{12}$

g) $\frac{1}{6}, \frac{2}{6}, \frac{3}{6}, \frac{5}{6}$

h) $\frac{2}{9}, \frac{5}{9}, \frac{7}{9}, \frac{9}{9}$

2 a) $\frac{1}{4}, \frac{3}{8}, \frac{2}{4}, \frac{6}{8}$

b) $\frac{1}{6}, \frac{2}{6}, \frac{1}{2}, \frac{6}{6}$

c) $\frac{1}{6}, \frac{1}{3}, \frac{3}{6}, \frac{2}{3}$

d) $\frac{1}{3} = \frac{2}{6}, \frac{1}{2}, \frac{3}{3}$

e) $\frac{1}{5}, \frac{3}{5}, \frac{8}{10}, \frac{9}{10}$

f) $\frac{1}{4}, \frac{3}{8}, \frac{3}{4}, \frac{7}{8}$

Challenge

a) More than half =

$\frac{5}{6}, \frac{3}{3}, \frac{2}{3}, \frac{8}{12}, \frac{4}{5}, \frac{3}{4}$

Less than half = $\frac{1}{6}, \frac{2}{10}, \frac{2}{5}, \frac{3}{8}$

b) >; <; >

Fractions with a total of 1 (page 19)

1 a) $\frac{2}{6} + \frac{4}{6} = \frac{6}{6}$ or 1

b) $\frac{10}{12} + \frac{2}{12} = \frac{12}{12}$ or 1

c) $\frac{1}{5} + \frac{4}{5} = \frac{5}{5}$ or 1

d) $\frac{4}{10} + \frac{6}{10} = \frac{10}{10}$ or 1

e) $\frac{1}{3} + \frac{2}{3} = \frac{3}{3}$ or 1

f) $\frac{8}{16} + \frac{8}{16} = \frac{16}{16}$ or 1

2 a) $\frac{2}{5} + \frac{3}{5} = \frac{5}{5}$ or 1

b) $\frac{2}{3} + \frac{1}{3} = \frac{3}{3}$ or 1

c) $\frac{1}{4} + \frac{3}{4} = \frac{4}{4}$ or 1

d) $\frac{16}{20} + \frac{4}{20} = \frac{20}{20}$ or 1

e) $\frac{8}{10} + \frac{2}{10} = \frac{10}{10}$ or 1

Challenge

a) Answers will vary but pairs should equal 1.
b) Answers will vary but pairs should equal 1.

Adding fractions with common denominator (page 21)

a) $\frac{3}{4}$

b) $\frac{7}{8}$

c) $\frac{6}{6}$ or 1

d) $\frac{6}{10}$

e) $\frac{5}{6}$

f) $\frac{7}{8}$

a) $\frac{4}{6}$

b) $\frac{5}{8}$

c) $\frac{5}{6}$

d) $\frac{1}{4}$

Challenge

a) $\frac{7}{9}$

b) $\frac{8}{8}$ or 1

c) $\frac{6}{12}$ or $\frac{1}{2}$

d) $\frac{7}{12}$

Subtracting fractions with a common denominator (page 23)

1 a) $\frac{3}{5}$

b) $\frac{1}{8}$

c) $\frac{1}{6}$

d) $\frac{1}{6}$

e) $\frac{5}{8}$

f) $\frac{0}{6}$ or 0

2 a) $\frac{0}{8}$ or 0

b) $\frac{4}{8}$

c) $\frac{1}{10}$

d) $\frac{1}{4}$

Challenge

a) $\frac{1}{4}$

b) $\frac{2}{3}$

c) $\frac{3}{5}$

Decimal notation (page 25)

1 0.1 = one tenth; 0.4 = four tenths;
0.8 = zero point 8; 1.3 = one and three tenths; 1.4 = fourteen tenths; 3.1 = three and 1 tenth;
5.9 = five and nine tenths; 7.6 = seven point six;
17.5 = seventeen and five tenths;
31 = thirty-one

2 a) 7

b) 50

c) seven tenths

d) five tenths

e) two hundredths

f) five hundredths

Challenge

a) 0.83 0.06 0.55 0.62

b) Examples: 35.0 3.50 3.05 0.35 53.0 5.30 5.03 0.53

Decimals in money (page 27)

1 a) £2 36p

b) £5 5p

c) £10 75p

d) £0 1p

e) £0 54p

f) £18 7p

g) £0 10p

h) £6 0p

2 a) £15.43

b) £8.34

c) £16.65

d) £5.99

e) £24.10

Challenge

a) ×10

b) ÷100

c) +0.27

d) +0.04
52p + £2.85 = £3.37; 52p + £11.39 = £11.91
52p + 92p = £1.44; £2.85 + £11.39 = £14.24
£2.85 + 92p = £3.77; £11.39 + 92p = £12.31

Converting pounds to pence and vice versa (page 29)

1 a) £1.52

b) 63p

c) 199p

d) £0.85

e) £2.37

f) £15.75

g) 709p

h) £9.99

i) 1050p

j) 2500p

2 a) £12.02 or 1202p

b) £27.37 or 2737p

c) £1.48 or 148p

d) £22.84 or 2284p

e) £11.98 or 1198p

Challenge

a) £15.09

b) 4617p

c) sunglasses, train and headphones:
237p + 709p + 999p = 1945p

Decimals in length (page 31)

1 a) 4 m 21 cm

b) 9 m 6 cm

c) 12 m 56 cm

d) 0 m 2 cm

e) 0 m 32 cm

f) 24 m 9 cm

g) 12 m 0 cm

h) 0 m 10 cm

2 a) 3.61 m

b) 13.8 m

c) 8.1 m

d) 22.62 m

e) 4.47 m

Challenge

a) and b)
45.69 m 45.96 m 46.59 m 46.95 m 49.56 m
49.65 m 54.69 m 54.96 m 56.49 m 56.94 m
59.46 m 59.64 m 64.59 m 64.95 m 65.49 m
65.94 m 69.45 m 69.54 m 94.56 m 94.65 m
95.46 m 95.64 m 96.45 m 96.54 m

Converting metres to centimetres and vice versa (page 33)

1 a) 1.4 m
b) 1.9 m
c) 0.6 m
d) 0.8 m
e) 1.1 m
f) 2.1 m

2 a) 70 cm
b) 80 cm
c) 130 cm
d) 150 cm
e) 190 cm
f) 200 cm

Challenge

a) 240 cm
b) 1.6 m
c) 290 cm

Equivalence between decimals and fractions (page 35)

1 a) $\frac{6}{10}$ and 0.6
b) $\frac{4}{10}$ and 0.4
c) $\frac{2}{10}$ and 0.2
d) $\frac{1}{10}$ or 0.1
e) $\frac{5}{10}$ or 0.5

2 a) $\frac{9}{10}$
b) $1\frac{4}{10}$
c) $\frac{1}{10}$
d) $2\frac{6}{10}$
e) $\frac{5}{10}$
f) $2\frac{75}{100}$
g) $\frac{3}{10}$
h) $2\frac{8}{10}$

Challenge

a) 0.3 0.03 0.9 0.09 0.5 0.05
b) $\frac{4}{10}$ = 0.4 $\frac{5}{10}$ = 0.5 $\frac{6}{10}$ = 0.6 $\frac{7}{10}$ =
0.7 $\frac{8}{10}$ = 0.8 $\frac{9}{10}$ = 0.9 $\frac{10}{10}$ = 1

The number after the decimal point is the same number as the numerator.

Ordering decimals (page 37)

1 a)
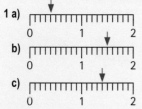

b)

c)

d)

e)

f)

g)

h)

2 a) 5.2, 6.2, 6.3, 6.9, 7.5
b) £0.8 = 80p, 88p, £8, £8.08, 888p
c) 2.5 cm, 25 cm, 2.05 m, 2.5 m, 25 m
d) 13 g, 130 g, 1.3 kg, 13 kg, 1300 kg
e) 22 ml, 220 ml, 2.0 l, 2.2 l, 220 l

Challenge

a) 15 steps
b) 11.1
c) <; >; >

Real life problems (page 39)

1 a) 3:22pm
b) 2.7 l
c) 6 buttons
d) $\frac{4}{5}$ of cake

2 a) 7 stickers
b) 9 mice
c) 51 biscuits
d) 1.2 l or 1200 ml

Challenge

a) 6 red marbles
b) 0.75
c) 60 have sandwiches

Problems involving money (page 41)

1 a) £9
b) 1300p
c) 690p
d) 150p

2 a) £2
b) £16
c) £1.18
d) £2000

Challenge

a) £11.01
b) 2225p
c) £59

Problems involving measures (page 43)

1 a) 5.47 m
b) 1.5 m or 150 m
c) 33 cm
d) 250 ml

2 a) 2.4 kg
b) 5.27 m
c) 9.24 kg
d) 300 ml

Challenge

a) 9166 cm
b) 2.45 l
c) 2.5 kg

1 Can you solve these fraction subtractions?

a) $\dfrac{4}{5} - \dfrac{2}{10} =$ [ ]

b) $\dfrac{5}{8} - \dfrac{2}{4} =$ [ ]

c) $\dfrac{5}{6} - \dfrac{2}{3} =$ [ ]

d) $\dfrac{5}{6} - \dfrac{2}{3} =$ [ ]

e) $\dfrac{7}{8} - \dfrac{1}{4} =$ [ ]

f) $\dfrac{4}{6} - \dfrac{2}{3} =$ [ ]

2 Draw pictures to help you work out these fraction subtractions.

a) $\dfrac{4}{8} - \dfrac{2}{4} =$ [ ]

b) $\dfrac{6}{8} - \dfrac{1}{4} =$ [ ]

c) $\dfrac{3}{10} - \dfrac{1}{5} =$ [ ]

d) $\dfrac{3}{4} - \dfrac{1}{2} =$ [ ]

CHALLENGE

Can you work out which fraction has been taken away?

a) $\dfrac{5}{8} - \dfrac{\boxed{}}{4} = \dfrac{3}{8}$

b) $\dfrac{5}{6} - \dfrac{\boxed{}}{3} = \dfrac{1}{6}$

c) $\dfrac{8}{10} - \dfrac{\boxed{}}{5} = \dfrac{2}{10}$

Decimal notation

Decimals are smaller parts of a whole number. The number before a decimal point is a whole number. The first digit after the decimal point shows the number of tenths and the second digit indicates the hundredths.

- 57.9 is 57 and 9 tenths

- 23.27 is 23 and 2 tenths and 7 hundredths OR 23 and 27 tenths

What is the 9 digit worth in 24.92?

1 Have another look. Read the question again.

Look at the number and the decimal point.

2 Ask yourself what they want you to find out.

I need to find how much the 9 digit is worth. Where is the decimal point?

3 Look at how you can solve it.

24 is the whole number as it is before the decimal point. 92 is after the decimal point, so this is a fraction of a whole. The 9 represents 9 parts of a whole that has been divided into ten equal parts.

4 Final answer. Is it correct?

The 9 digit is worth 9 tenths.

tips   Hints and tips   Hints and tips   Hints and tips   Hints and tips   Hints and t

- You need to understand the place value of each digit.   Th H T U . Tth Hth
- Zeros after the last number in a decimal fraction make no difference to the value,
  so 0.9 = 0.90 = 0.900.
- But if a zero after the decimal point is followed by another number, it does.

1 Join the numbers that are the same.

0.4

one tenth

1.4

four tenths

5.9

thirty-one

zero point 8

one and three tenths

17.5

7.6

0.8

3.1

seventeen and five tenths

five and nine tenths

seven point six

1.3

0.1

three and 1 tenth

31

fourteen tenths

2 Write down what each blue digit is worth.

a) 17.0 =

b) 56.3 =

c) 0.7 =

d) 23.56 =

e) 9.32 =

f) 132.65 =

CHALLENGE

a) Write these fractions as decimals.

$\frac{83}{100}$

$\frac{6}{100}$

$\frac{55}{100}$

$\frac{62}{100}$

b)

0   5   3

Using these digit cards and a decimal point, how many different decimal numbers can you make?

Decimals in money

These questions will ask you to write amounts in pounds and pence. You may need to add a number of coins together to give a total. Remember to use either £ or p.

Write the total of four £1 coins, one 50p coin, two 10p coins and one 5p coin.

1 Have another look. Read the question again.

Look carefully at the amount of coins.

2 Ask yourself what they want you to find out.

I must find the total of the listed coins. That means I must add all the coins together.

3 Look at how you can solve it.

Start with the highest coin amount.
Four £1 = £4.00
One 50p = 50p
Two 10p = 20p
One 5p = 5p
Add the totals together.

4 Final answer. Is it correct?

£4.00 + 50p + 20p + 5p = £4.75

- Remember that the digit before the decimal point gives you the number of pounds and the two digits after the decimal point give you the number of pence.
- 100p = £1

1 How many pounds and pence are in these amounts?

a) £2.36   £ [ ]   p [ ]   **b)** £5.05   £ [ ]   p [ ]

c) £10.75 £ [ ]   p [ ]   **d)** £0.01   £ [ ]   p [ ]

e) £0.54   £ [ ]   p [ ]   **f)** £18.07 £ [ ]   p [ ]

g) £0.10   £ [ ]   p [ ]   **h)** £6.00   £ [ ]   p [ ]

2 Write the totals in pounds and pence.

a) Thirteen £1 coins, four 50p coins, two 20p coins, three 1p coins [ ]

b) Seven £1 coins, six 20p coins, two 5p coins, two 2p coins [ ]

c) Fifteen £1 coins, one 50p coin, eleven 10p coins, one 5p coin [ ]

d) Three £1 coins, three 50p coins, seven 20p coins, nine 1p coins [ ]

e) Twenty-two £1 coins, one 50p coin, eight 20p coins [ ]

CHALLENGE

Work out how these prices change. You can only use one operation for each one. E.g. to change £67 to £6.70 you ÷ 10.

a) 65p to £6.50 [ ]

b) £534 to £5.34 [ ]

c) £3.25 to £3.52 [ ]

d) £2.12 to £2.16 [ ]

Choose two cards from the ones below and find the total. How many different totals can you find by using two different cards each time?

£2.85   92p

52p   £11.39

Converting pounds to pence and vice versa

These questions ask you to write your answers in pounds or pence.

- If the answer is in pounds you need to use the pound sign (£) and the decimal point.

- If the answer is in pence, you do not need a decimal point and you must remember the pence sign (p).

Write 207p in pounds.

1 *Have* another look. Read the question again.

Read slowly and carefully.

2 *Ask* yourself what they want you to find out.

I need to write 207p in pounds. I must use a £ sign and decimal point in this answer.

3 *Look* at how you can solve it.

207p is the same as 200p + 7p. I can write 200p as £2 followed by a decimal point. I must then write 7p.

7p is the same as $\frac{7}{100}$ of a pound. £2.7 is the same as £2 and 70p. This is NOT right!
£2.07 is the same as £2 and 7p. This is correct!

4 *Final* answer. Is it correct?

Yes, £2.07 is the same as:
200p + 0 tenths (0 tens)
+ 7 hundredths (7 ones)

tips Hints and tips Hints and tips Hints and tips Hints and tips Hints and t

- 100p = £1.00

- The digit before the decimal point tells you the number of pounds.

- The digits after the decimal point give you parts of a pound (the number of pence).

1 Look at the prices on the items below. Write each price in pounds or pence.

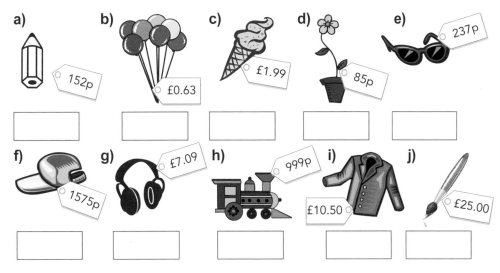

a) 152p

b) £0.63

c) £1.99

d) 85p

e) 237p

f) 1575p

g) £7.09

h) 999p

i) £10.50

j) £25.00

2 Find the total cost of the items below. Write your answers in pounds and then pence.

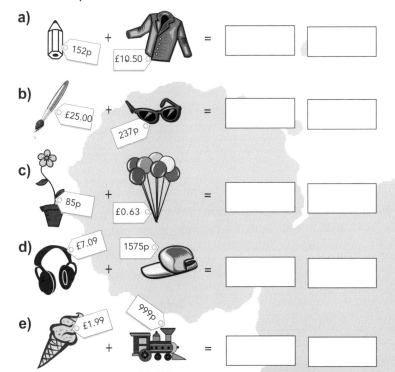

a) 152p + £10.50 = [ ] [ ]

b) £25.00 + 237p = [ ] [ ]

c) 85p + £0.63 = [ ] [ ]

d) £7.09 + 1575p = [ ] [ ]

e) £1.99 + 999p = [ ] [ ]

CHALLENGE

a) Write in £ the total of fifteen £1 coins and nine 1p coins.

b) Write the total of two £20 notes, six £1 coins, three 5p coins and two 1p coins. Write your answer in p.

c) Look at the items in question 1. Which three items total 1945p?

Decimals in length

Length questions may include short lengths (in mm and cm) and longer lengths (in m and km).

You may need to add a number of lengths together to give a total. Remember to use mm, cm, m or km in your answer.

Find the total length of 12.2 m and 15 cm. Write your answer in metres.

1 Have another look. Read the question again.	Total means add. This is an addition question.
2 Ask yourself what they want you to find out.	I need to add the two lengths together. To make it easier I need to use the same units of measurement. I need to convert one.
3 Look at how you can solve it.	I shall use cm. 12.2 m is the same as 1220 cm. 1220 cm + 15 cm = 1235 cm Now I need to convert 1235 cm into metres. 1235 cm = 12.35 m
4 Final answer. Is it correct?	12.2 m + 15 cm = 12.35 m

tips   Hints and tips   Hints and tips   Hints and tips   Hints and tips   Hints and t

- Remember the different units for length:
  10 mm = 1 cm = 0.01 m
  100 mm = 10 cm = 0.1 m
  1000 mm = 100 cm = 1 m

- If you take the decimal point away to make your working out easier, remember to replace it at the end.

1 How many metres and centimetres make up these lengths?

	metres	*centimetres*			*metres*	*centimetres*
a) 4.21 m			**b)** 9.06 m			
c) 12.56 m			**d)** 0.02 m			
e) 0.32 m			**f)** 24.09 m			
g) 12 m			**h)** 0.10 m			

2 Add up the following lengths and write your answers in metres.

a) 1 m 45 cm + 2 m 16 cm = ☐ m

b) 6 m 74 cm + 7 m 6 cm = ☐ m

c) 5 m 80 cm + 2 m 30 cm = ☐ m

d) 4 m 9 cm + 18 m 53 cm = ☐ m

e) 82 cm + 3 m 65 cm = ☐ m

CHALLENGE

4	9	5	6

a) Look at the four cards above. How many different lengths can you make that have two digits after the decimal point? Write your answers in metres, e.g. 56.49 m.

b) Now write the numbers in order, starting with the lowest.

Converting metres to centimetres and vice versa

These questions ask you to write your answers in metres or centimetres. If the answer is in metres you need to use the metre sign (m) and the decimal point. If the answer is in centimetres, you do not need a decimal point and you must remember to put cm at the end.

Write 268 cm in metres.

1 | *Have* another look. Read the question again. | Read the question slowly and carefully.

2 | *Ask* yourself what they want you to find out. | I need to write 268 cm in metres. I must use a decimal point and the unit "m" at the end.

3 | *Look* at how you can solve it. | I can draw a chart.

100 cm	1 m
200 cm	2 m

I know that there are 2 complete metres in 268 cm and that leaves 68 cm.

4 | *Final* answer. Is it correct? | The answer must be 2.68 m as there are 2 complete metres and 68 hundredths of a metre left (or 68 cm).

tips   **Hints and tips**   **Hints and tips**   **Hints and tips**   **Hints and tips**   **Hints and t**

- If the answer is in metres, the digit before the decimal point gives you the number of complete metres. The digits after the decimal point give you the number of tenths and hundredths of a metre (the number of centimetres).

- "Centi" means 100. There are 100 centimetres in a metre.

1 Write the length of each plank of wood in metres.

a)
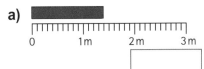

b)
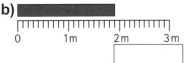

c)

d)

e)
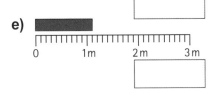

f)
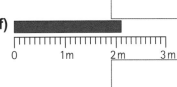

2 Write the length of each ribbon in centimetres.

a)

b)

c)

d)

e)

f)

CHALLENGE

The line below shows how far Natalie jumped in the long-jump competition.

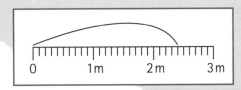

a) How far did Natalie jump? Write your answer in centimetres.

b) Victoria jumped zero point eight metres less than Natalie. How far did she jump? Write your answer in metres.

c) Philip jumped one point three metres further than Victoria. How far did he jump? Write your answer in centimetres.

Equivalence between decimals and fractions

Fractions and decimals are both part of a whole but they are written differently.

$$0.5 = \frac{5}{10} = \frac{50}{100}$$

Write $\frac{3}{10}$ as a decimal.

1 Have another look. Read the question again.

Read the question again. Look at the fraction.

2 Ask yourself what they want you to find out.

I need to write $\frac{3}{10}$ as a decimal. That means using a decimal point in my answer. $\frac{3}{10}$ means three tenths of a whole.

3 Look at how you can solve it.

$\frac{3}{10}$ is not a whole number. It is 3 parts of a whole that has been divided into tenths. So the digit before the decimal point is 0. The digit after the decimal point tells you the number of tenths, so $\frac{3}{10}$ must be 0.3.

4 Final answer. Is it correct?

I can check on a number line.

Yes, $\frac{3}{10}$ is equivalent to 0.3!

tips   Hints and tips   Hints and tips   Hints and tips   Hints and tips   Hints and t

• A number line can be used to check your answers.

0   0.1   0.2   0.3   0.4   0.5   0.6   0.7   0.8   0.9   1

$\frac{1}{10}$ $\frac{2}{10}$ $\frac{3}{10}$ $\frac{4}{10}$ $\frac{5}{10}$ $\frac{6}{10}$ $\frac{7}{10}$ $\frac{8}{10}$ $\frac{9}{10}$

1 Write the shaded part as a fraction and as a decimal.

a)   **b)**   **c)**   **d)**   **e)**

 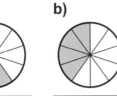 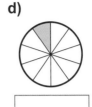 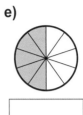

 2 Use the number line on page 34 to help you answer these questions. Write the equivalent fraction for each of these decimals.

a) 0.9   **b)** 1.4

c) 0.1   **d)** 2.6

e) 0.5   **f)** 2.75

g) 0.3   **h)** 2.8

CHALLENGE

a) Write the equivalent decimals of these fractions.

$\frac{3}{10}$ ☐ $\frac{3}{100}$ ☐ $\frac{9}{10}$ ☐ $\frac{9}{100}$ ☐ $\frac{5}{10}$ ☐ $\frac{5}{100}$ ☐

b) You need a calculator for this question. $\frac{1}{10}$ is another way of writing 1 ÷ 10. We can find equivalent fractions on a calculator.

Use a calculator to find the equivalent decimals. Continue the pattern. What do you notice?

Fraction	$\frac{1}{10}$	$\frac{2}{10}$	$\frac{3}{10}$							
Decimal	0.1	0.2	0.3							

Ordering decimals

Ordering decimals may involve putting numbers of any unit in order, e.g. money in pounds, length in metres, weights in kilograms, etc.

Put these decimals in order, starting with the smallest:

3.3, 2.5, 1.2, 1.6, 2.7

1 *Have* another look. Read the question again.

Read the question slowly and carefully. Look at the decimals.

2 *Ask* yourself what they want you to find out.

I need to put the decimals in order starting with the smallest.

3 *Look* at how you can solve it.

First I need to look at the digit before the decimal point as that is a whole number. I know that 1 comes before 2 and 3. Next I need to look at the tenths.
1.2 is lower than 1.6.
2.5 is lower than 2.7.
3.3 is the highest number.

4 *Final* answer. Is it correct?

Let's check on the number line.
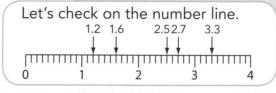

If you need to order numbers of mixed units, e.g. m and cm, it may be easier to convert them into the same unit first.
E.g. 8.5 m, 8.05 m, 85 m, 85 cm, 8.5 cm = 8.5 m, 8.05 m, 85 m, 0.85 m, 0.085 m

1 Place these decimals on the number lines.

a) 0.4

0   1   2

b) 1.5

0   1   2

c) 1.4

0   1   2

d) 1.8

0   1   2

e) 1.2

0   1   2

f) 0.1

0   1   2

g) 0.9

0   1   2

h) 0.7

0   1   2

2 Put these numbers in order starting with the smallest.

a) 6.2, 7.5, 6.3, 5.2, 6.9

b) 88p, £8, 80p, £8.08, 888p, £0.8

c) 2.5m, 2.05m, 25m, 25cm, 2.5cm

d) 1.3kg, 13kg, 130g, 13g, 1300kg

e) 22ml, 2.0l, 220ml, 220l, 2.2l

CHALLENGE

a) Start at 1.3 and count up in steps of one tenth. Finish at 2.8. How many steps did you count?

b) Start at 12.6 and count back fifteen tenths. What number do you finish on?

c) Write < or > between each pair of decimals.

6.09 ☐ 6.9

3.2 ☐ 2.3

12.01 ☐ 2.10

Real life problems

These problems involve fractions and decimals in everyday situations. Some problems may have more than one step. Try to work out what each step is asking you to do before you complete it.

A shop has 4 pizzas. Each pizza is cut into eighths.

The shop sells 25 eighths. How many eighths are left?

1 *Have* another look. Read the question again.

Look at the numbers.

2 *Ask* yourself what they want you to find out.

I need to divide 4 pizzas into eighths. I then need to take 25 eighths away and count how many eighths are left.

3 *Look* at how you can solve it.

I could draw 4 pizzas and divide each of them into 8 pieces. If I colour 25 eighths it will show me how many eighths are left.

4 *Final* answer. Is it correct?

There are 7 eighths not coloured, so the answer must be 7.

Hints and tips Hints and tips Hints and tips Hints and tips Hints and tips Hints and t

- Drawing pictures can help with fraction problems.
- Work out one step at a time.
- Your times tables will help you with some of these questions.

1

a) The race started at 3:15pm and lasted 7 minutes. What time did it finish?

b) John had 1.2 litres of orange juice and James had 1.5 litres of apple juice. How much juice did they have altogether?

c) The dressmaker had 24 buttons. She sewed a quarter of them onto a dress. How many buttons did she use?

d) A shop has 3 cakes. Each cake is cut into fifths. The shop sells 11 fifths. How many fifths are left?

2

a) Molly had 56 stickers. She gave an eighth of them to Meg. How many did Meg get?

b) There are 30 chocolate mice in a box. Simon eats three-tenths of them. How many chocolate mice does he eat?

c) A box holds 68 biscuits. A quarter of them are eaten. How many are left?

d) The bottle of tomato sauce holds 300 ml. How much in l and ml do 4 bottles hold?

CHALLENGE

a) Sarah has 30 marbles. Half are yellow, 6 are green and one third of the rest are blue. The others are red. How many marbles are red?

b) Stacey uses her calculator to find. $3 \div 4 =$

What decimal will appear on her calculator?

c) There are 72 children at the party. Half of them have cheese sandwiches and one third of them have ham sandwiches. How many children have sandwiches?

Problems involving money

Money problems will include mixed units of pounds and pence.

They can involve adding, subtracting, multiplying or dividing.

Zoë was given £24 for her birthday. She spent a quarter of it on a new pencil case and spent another £10 on a new jumper. How much did she have left?

1 *Have* another look. Read the question again.

Look at the numbers and the fraction.

2 *Ask* yourself what they want you to find out.

This is a division and subtraction sum. I need to know how much money Zoë had left after buying a pencil case and a jumper.

3 *Look* at how you can solve it.

I need to find the price of the pencil case. A quarter is the same as dividing by 4.
$24 \div 4 = 6$
Zoë spent £6 on the pencil case. Now subtract £6 from £24.
£24 – £6 = £18
Now take another £10 off for the jumper.
£18 – £10 = £8

4 *Final* answer. Is it correct?

Zoë had £8 left.

tips **Hints and tips** Hints and tips Hints and tips Hints and tips Hints and t

- There are 100 pence (p) in one pound (£).
- Remember to use the £ or p units.

1

a) Thomas had £18 to spend. He spent half of it. How much did he have left?

b) The shop had a half price sale. Harry bought a toy in the sale for £6.50. What was the original price? Write your answer in pence.

c) Three books cost £1.30, £2.50 and £3.10. How much did they cost altogether? Write your answer in pence.

d) Bradley had £2. He spent a quarter of it on a jigsaw puzzle. How much change did he get? Write your answer in pence.

2

a) In the cake shop, a chocolate gateau costs £12. It is divided into sixths. How much does one piece cost?

b) A shop has a sale. The cost of the shopping is rounded down to the nearest £. Sita's bill came to £16.38. How much did she actually pay?

c) Alex had 500p. He spent 230p on a comic and £1.52 on a set of stickers. How much money did he have left? Write your answer in £.

d) A group of people won £16,000 on the lottery. Each person received $\frac{1}{8}$ of the total. How much money did each person receive?

CHALLENGE

a) James had £20 and he spent 899p on a jumper. How much change did he get? Write your answer in pounds.

b) Ben bought 2 tickets for the theatre. He paid with a £50 note. His change was £5.50. How much did one ticket cost? Write your answer in pence.

c) Claire bought 4 chairs at a cost of £14.85 each. What was the total cost to the nearest £?

Problems involving measures

Problems that involve measures usually include decimal points. They may be about time, length or capacity.

Russell has 1.3 m of rope. He cuts off 50 cm. How much rope is left?

1 *Have* another look. Read the question again.

Look at the numbers and units. These measurements are different units (m and cm).

It will be easier if I make them the same. I'll use cm.

1.3 m = 130 cm

2 *Ask* yourself what they want you to find out.

How much rope is left? I have to do a subtraction sum.

3 *Look* at how you can solve it.

I can draw a picture or use a number line. Russell has 130 cm to start with and 50 cm is cut off.
130 – 50 = 80 cm

0 10 20 30 40 50 60 70 80 90 100 110 120 130

4 *Final* answer. Is it correct?

Let's check by adding.
80 cm + 50 cm = 130 cm
Yes, it's right. You could write the answer in cm (80 cm) or m (0.80 m).

tips Hints and tips Hints and tips Hints and tips Hints and tips Hints and t

- Always look at the units, e.g. cm, m, l, ml.
- If the measurements are in different units, convert one to make them the same.

1

a) The pole measures 6 m. It is 53 cm too long. How long should the pole be?

b) A high jumper jumped 110 cm. On his second jump he jumped 0.4 m higher. How high did he jump on his second attempt?

c) Lucy's hair ribbon measures 0.50 m. She cuts off 17 cm. How much ribbon does she have left?

d) Chloe shares her 1 litre bottle of lemonade. She gives half to her brother and a quarter to her Mum. How many ml does she have left?

2

a) 6 cans of soup are needed to make lunch. Each can contains 400 g. How much soup is there altogether? Write your answer in kg.

b) The plank of wood measures 5.8 m. It is 53 cm too long. How long should the plank of wood be?

c) The sack of potatoes weighs 9 kg and the bag of oranges weighs 240 g. What is the total weight?

d) David shares his 2 litre bottle of coke. He gives half to his sister, a quarter to his brother and a tenth to his friend. How many ml does he have left?

CHALLENGE

a) Gillian takes part in the javelin competition. Her first throw measures 29.2 m, her second throw measures 32.4 m and her third throw measures 30.06 m. What is the total of all three throws in cm?

b) Gemma has 2 litres of coke, Imogen has 1.25 litres of lemonade and Jessica has 700 ml of orange squash. They each drink 500 ml of their own drink. How much drink do they have left altogether?

c) A potato weighs about 250 g. Roughly how much do 10 potatoes weigh? Write your answer in kg.

The Skills Builders Range

Grammar and Punctuation

   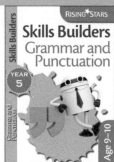 

Spelling and Vocabulary

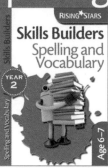  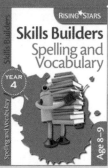 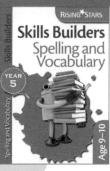 

Times Tables

Fractions, Decimals and Percentages

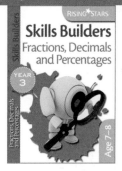  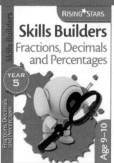